EASY
VOCABULARY
GAMES

for Beginning English Language Learners

EASY VOCABULARY GAMES

for Beginning English Language Learners

Linda Schinke-Llano

Illustrated by
Kelly Flint

National Textbook Company
a division of *NTC Publishing Group* • Lincolnwood, Illinois USA

To The Teacher

The blackline masters in
this book may be
photocopied or
reproduced using infrared
copying techniques.

1990 Printing

Published by National Textbook Company, a division of NTC Publishing Group.
© 1987 by NTC Publishing Group, 4255 West Touhy Avenue,
Lincolnwood (Chicago), Illinois 60646-1975 U.S.A.
Manufactured in the United States of America.

0 ML 9 8 7 6 5 4 3 2

CONTENTS

	Master Number
To the Teacher	
Answer Key	
Who Am I?	1
Riddles	2
Prepositions	3
Let's Compare	4
The Telephone	5
Verb Fit-In	6
Opposites	7
Time	8
Build A Word	9
Relationships	10
Where Are You?	11
Word Stairs	12
Animals	13
2 + 2	14
Money	15
The Bus Station	16
Cars	17
Two-Word Verbs	18
At the Restaurant	19
Signs	20
Adjectives	21
Pairs	22
Adverbs	23
Schedules	24
Crossword Verbs	25
Backward/Forward Words	26
The Movies	27
Television	28
Fast Food and Snacks	29
The Post Office	30
Music! Music! Music!	31
At the Bank	32

TO THE TEACHER

The enclosed set of blackline masters contains 32 word games designed for beginning students of English as a second or foreign language at the junior and senior high school levels. Intended as supplementary activities, the games can be used to review and reinforce everyday vocabulary, including verbs and useful expressions. Individual pages may be employed immediately following related lessons in basal series, or later as spot-checks to see if students have retained the information presented in daily lessons. Appropriate for individual as well as group work, the vocabulary games can be utilized in class or as brief take-home assignments. They are especially useful in the mixed-level class which is so prevalent in ESL programs. In all instances, the activities are intended to provide students with an enjoyable alternative for review and to save teachers time by supplying ready-to-use supplementary material.

Basal ESL series commonly used at the junior and senior high school levels were consulted in order to keep vocabulary and structures appropriate for the targeted groups. Whenever possible, items are presented in context in an effort to aid comprehension and retention. At times the context is deliberately cultural, since learning a second language involves learning a second culture as well. All pages have directions, and the majority have examples for the students. Most games are self-correcting; in addition, answers for each game are provided in the Answer Key section of this book.

With respect to directions to the students, an effort was made to keep the language as simple as possible, especially in earlier pages. Certain expressions, however, are unavoidable. Therefore, it is suggested that the teacher include an explanation of key directional terms prior to assigning activities. Since comprehension of directions is crucial to completing assignments correctly, this preparation will help students not only with the vocabulary games in this book, but also with assignments in their content area classes. Words and expressions used frequently in the directions are as follows:

Fill in the blanks...	Puzzle
Circle...	Underlined words
Complete the sentences...	Alphabetical order
Unscramble the letters...	Correct form
Match...	Verbs
Answer the questions...	Opposites
Change the first letter...	Pairs
Draw a line...	Adjectives
Count...	Adverbs
Rewrite...	
Find...	
Put in order...	

Twenty-two different types of games are used, as well as combinations and variations of several. If students are unfamiliar with such word games, it may be necessary to work through some of the most common as group activities. The following are suggested:

1. *Anagrams:* (See #13 as an example.) Anagrams are presented in context to assist students in decoding.

2. *Hidden words:* (See #28.) Such puzzles are based on a theme. Words in the puzzle may be found horizontally or vertically.

3. *Fill-ins:* (See #10.) Fill-in items are presented in context and are self-correcting. Most fill-in activities are coupled with numerically referenced puzzles of sayings or sentences.

4. *Fit-ins:* (See #6.) Fit-ins are self-correcting in that incorrect words won't fit in the puzzle. In addition, most fit-in puzzles spell out a theme word when correctly finished or are coupled with numerically referenced puzzles.

5. *Inside words:* (See #31.) Words chosen are related to a theme. Students make new words by recombining letters of the cue word. Although many new words could be made from each cue, it is expected that students will find the most common letter combinations. Therefore, they are asked to make a minimal number of words for each cue. This exercise is useful in acquainting students with word formation practices in English, and teachers may wish to expand the activity if students are successful with it.

6. *Crossword puzzles:* (See #19.) Puzzles are related to a theme to aid students in identifying the proper words. The words "across" and "down" are used instead of "horizontal" and "vertical."

For more advanced classes, the author has created two companion books of blackline masters, *Vocabulary Games for Intermediate English Language Learners,* and *Advanced Vocabulary Games for English Language Learners.*

ANSWER KEY

Master 1:   WHO AM I?

1. teacher
2. barber
3. fire fighter
4. garbage collector
5. mail carrier
6. policeman
7. dentist
8. doctor
9. farmer
10. cook

Master 2:   RIDDLES

1. pan
2. dish
3. tub
4. car
5. pen
6. toy
7. mop
8. lamp
9. book
10. cat
11. dog
12. house
13. coat
14. pool
15. milk

Master 3:   PREPOSITIONS

1. on
2. beside
3. under
4. on top of
5. in front of
6. in
7. above
8. around
9. beneath

Master 4:   LET'S COMPARE

1. Rita, Carol
2. Tom, George
3. House B, House A
4. Sparky, Jocko
5. Bob, Jim
6. Mary's car, Ken's car
7. B
8. C
9. A
10. A

Master 5:   THE TELEPHONE

1. dial
2. receiver
3. cord
4. coin slot
5. coin return

Master 6:   VERB FIT–IN

1. KEPT
2. RANG
3. LOST
4. SAT
5. MET
6. SENT
7. WON
8. SOLD
9. WORE
10. DROVE
11. ATE
12. FORGOT
13. BOUGHT
14. SWAM

Master 7:   OPPOSITES

1. w, l
2. g, t
3. b, s
4. w, p
5. s, s
6. a, a
7. r, l
8. a, a
9. d, w
10. a, b
11. d, l
12. c, h
13. p, u
14. n, o
15. s, h

Master 8:   TIME

1. two hours
2. one hour
3. one and one–half hours
4. four hours
5. thirty minutes
6. forty–five minutes
7. eight hours
8. six hours

Master 9:   BUILD A WORD

1. ants, pants
2. ear, hear
3. ring, string
4. pins, spins
5. car, scar
6. river, driver
7. pills, spills
8. light, flight
9. rain, drain
10. hat, that

Master 10:   RELATIONSHIPS

p
st
pa
cu
pl
su
au
te
ch
em
relationships

Master 11:   WHERE ARE YOU?

at the airport

Master 12:   WORD STAIRS

```
A C R O S S
        T
        U
        D
        Y E L L O W
              E
              E
            K N E E
              R
              A
              S
              E
            R O U N D
                  O
                  W
                N E X T
                    A
                    L
                  L U N C H
                        E
                        L
                        P
```

Master 13:   ANIMALS

1. ant
2. frog
3. elephant
4. horse
5. rabbit
6. zebra
7. owl
8. deer
9. cow
10. bird
11. chicken
12. butterfly

Master 14:   2 + 2

one and nine-tenths —— 1.9
one–half —— 1/2
multiply —— ×
equal —— =
add —— +
one–third —— 1/3
sixty–eight hundredths —— .68
divide —— ÷
fiftieth —— 50th
percent —— %
subtract —— –
two–sevenths —— 2/7
zero —— 0
two–fourths —— 2/4
four–thousandths —— .004

Master 15:   MONEY

PENNY
NICKEL
DIME
QUARTER
HALF DOLLAR
ONE DOLLAR BILL
FIVE DOLLAR BILL
TEN DOLLAR BILL
TWENTY DOLLAR BILL
FIFTY DOLLAR BILL
A PENNY SAVED IS A PENNY EARNED.

Master 16:   THE BUS STATION

1. ATLANTA
2. BOSTON
3. DALLAS
4. DENVER
5. LAS VEGAS
6. MIAMI
7. NEW ORLEANS
8. NEW YORK
9. PITTSBURGH
10. PORTLAND
11. SAN ANTONIO
12. SAN FRANCISCO
THE BUS LEAVES ON TIME!

Master 17:   CARS

hood   steering wheel   gas tank
windshield   roof   trunk   tail light
headlight   tire   door   door handle   bumper

Master 18:   TWO–WORD VERBS

1. up
2. back
3. down
4. through
5. out
6. up
7. back
8. on
9. up
10. up
11. off
12. out
13. over
14. down
15. in
correct!

Master 19:   AT THE RESTAURANT

Across:	Down:
1. tip	2. Coke
2. cold	3. dessert
4. coffee	4. cashier
6. steak	5. entree
11. menu	6. salad
12. cook	7. tea
13. salt	8. waiter
	10. lunch

Master 20:   SIGNS

R$_x$ —— drug store
Lead-free $1.27/gal. —— gas station
All Flights On Time —— airport
For Rent —— apartment
Next feature: 10 p.m. —— movie theater
Quiet Please! —— library
Speed Limit 55 mph —— highway
U.S. Mail —— post office
eggs 79¢/dozen —— supermarket
Don't Pick the Flowers —— park
Lot Filled —— parking lot
We have YOUR size! —— shoe store
Not For Hire —— taxi
Exact Change only —— bus
Open for Breakfast —— restaurant

Master 21:   ADJECTIVES

One Syllable:	1. fifth
	2. cheap
Two Syllables:	1. secret
	2. absent
	3. busy
	4. correct
Three Syllables:	1. underlined
	2. registered
	3. personal
Four Syllables:	1. intelligent
	2. educated
	3. horizontal

Master 22:   PAIRS

1. pepper
2. down
3. wrong
4. out
5. right
6. dogs
7. sister
8. leg
9. forth
10. uncle
11. short
12. bat
13. fork
14. day
15. shut
fine and dandy!

Master 23: ADVERBS

Answers will vary.

Master 24: SCHEDULES

R
I
G
H
T

RIGHT!

Master 25: CROSSWORD VERBS

Across:
3. sleep
5. understood
6. do
7. washes
9. were
11. will go
13. left
14. walked
15. speaks

Down:
1. studied
2. add
4. practices
8. be
12. was

Master 26: BACKWARD/ FORWARD WORDS

1. twelve o'clock in the day —— noon
2. something you drink —— pop
3. another word for <u>mother</u> —— mom
4. a tiny child —— tot
5. past tense of <u>do</u> —— did
6. something a baby wears —— bib
7. another name for <u>Robert</u> —— Bob
8. a call for help —— SOS
9. an exclamation —— Wow!
10. energy —— pep
11. short for <u>sister</u> —— sis
12. another word for <u>father</u> —— dad

Master 27: THE MOVIES

1. Everyone likes to go to the movies.
2. People prefer different kinds of movies.
3. My father likes Westerns.
4. My mother likes mysteries.
5. My brother prefers science fiction.
6. My sister chooses love stories.
7. My best friend always wants to see monster movies.
8. My other friends go to comedies.
9. I go to everything.
10. I love the popcorn.

Master 28: TELEVISION

Master 29: FAST FOOD AND SNACKS

donuts, coffee, cereal
hot dogs, hamburgers
french fries, soup
pizza, fried chicken
T.V. dinner
candy
popcorn, soft drinks
potato chips, pretzels

Master 30:   THE POST OFFICE

1. I went to the post office to mail a package.
2. I also wanted to buy some stamps.
3. The line was very long.
4. But it moved very quickly.
5. I sent the package first class.
6. The cost was $2.40.
7. I walked home slowly.
8. Then I remembered something.
9. I forgot to buy the stamps.
10. When I returned, the post office was closed.

Master 31:   MUSIC! MUSIC! MUSIC!

Answers will vary.

Master 32:   AT THE BANK

1. Yesterday I went to the bank.
2. I stood in line for fifteen minutes.
3. I asked the teller to cash my check.
4. He gave me twenties and tens.
5. Then I went to speak to one of the officers.
6. She helped me open a savings account.
7. The officer gave me a free gift for opening the account.
8. I'll go again next week.

NTC ESL/EFL TEXTS AND MATERIAL
Junior High—Adult Education

Computer Software
Amigo
Basic Vocabulary Builder on Computer

Language and Culture Readers
Beginner's English Reader
Passport to America series
  California Discovery
  Adventures in the Southwest
  The Coast-to-Coast Mystery
  The New York Connection
Discover America series (text/audio-
cassette)
  New York
  Chicago
  California
  Florida
  Washington, D.C.
  New England
  Hawaii
  Texas
Looking at American Signs
Looking at American Food
Looking at American Recreation
Looking at American Holidays
Time: We The People

**Text/Audiocassette Learning
Packages**
Speak Up! Sing Out! 1, 2
Listen and Say It Right in English!

Transparencies
Everyday Situations in English

**Duplicating Masters and
Blackline Masters**
Easy Vocabulary Games
Vocabulary Games
Advanced Vocabulary Games
Play and Practice!
Basic Vocabulary Builder
Practical Vocabulary Builder
Beginning Activities for English
  Language Learners
Intermediate Activities for English
  Language Learners
Advanced Activities for English
  Language Learners

Language-Skills Texts
English with a Smile 1, 2
The English Survival Series
  Building Vocabulary A, B, C
  Identifying Main Ideas A, B, C
  Recognizing Details A, B, C
  Using The Context A, B, C
  Writing Sentences and
  Paragraphs A, B, C

English Across the Curriculum 1, 2, 3
Essentials of Reading And Writing
  English 1, 2, 3
Everyday English 1, 2, 3, 4
Communication Skillbooks 1, 2, 3
Living in the U S A (3 Life Skills Readers)
Basic Everyday Spelling Workbook
Practical Everyday Spelling Workbook
Advanced Readings and Conversations
Real Writing
Express Yourself in Written English
Campus English
Speak English!
Read English!
Write English!
Orientation in American English
Building English Sentences
Grammar for Use
Grammar Step-by-Step
Reading by Doing
Speaking by Doing
Writing by Doing
Listening by Doing
Look, Think, and Write

Survival-Skills Texts
Building Real Life English Skills
Everyday Consumer English
Book of Forms
Essential Life Skills series
Finding a Job in The United States
English for Adult Living 1, 2
Living in English
Prevocational English

Dictionaries and References
Everyday American English Dictionary
Building Dictionary Skills in
  English (workbook)
Beginner's Dictionary of American
  English Usage
Beginner's English Dictionary
  Workbook
NTC's American Idioms Dictionary
NTC's Dictionary of American Slang
  and Colloquial Expressions
101 American English Idioms
Idiom Workbook
Essentials of English Grammar
The Complete ESL/EFL Resource Book
Safari Grammar
Safari Punctuation
TESOL Professional Anthology
  Grammar and Composition
  Listening, Speaking, and Reading
  Culture

For further information or a current catalog, write:
National Textbook Company
a division of NTC Publishing Group
4255 West Touhy Avenue
Lincolnwood, Illinois 60646-1975 U.S.A.

WHO AM I?

DIRECTIONS: Answer the questions. Use the pictures to help you.

Example: I bake cakes. Who am I?   _____baker_____

1. I teach school. Who am I?   _____

2. I cut hair. Who am I?   _____

3. I put out fires. Who am I?   _____

4. I pick up garbage. Who am I?   _____

5. I bring your mail. Who am I?   _____

6. I direct traffic. Who am I?   _____

7. I fix teeth. Who am I?   _____

8. I help sick people. Who am I?   _____

9. I grow your food. Who am I?   _____

10. I cook food. Who am I?   _____

RIDDLES

DIRECTIONS: Change the first letter. Make a new word.

Example: RED: Change the first letter.
                        Make something we sleep in.   _____bed_____

1. FAN   Change the first letter.
            Make something we cook in.   _____

2. FISH   Change the first letter.
            Make something we eat on.   _____

3. RUB   Change the first letter.
            Make something we take a bath in.   _____

4. FAR   Change the first letter.
            Make something we ride in.   _____

5. TEN   Change the first letter.
            Make something we write with.   _____

6. BOY   Change the first letter.
            Make something we play with.   _____

7. TOP   Change the first letter.
            Make something we clean the floor with.   _____

8. DAMP   Change the first letter.
            Make something that gives light.   _____

9. LOOK   Change the first letter.
            Make something that we read.   _____

10. FAT   Change the first letter.
            Make something that says "mee-ow."   _____

11. FOG   Change the first letter.
            Make something that barks.   _____

12. MOUSE   Change the first letter.
            Make something we live in.   _____

13. BOAT   Change the first letter.
            Make something we wear.   _____

14. COOL   Change the first letter.
            Make something we swim in.   _____

15. SILK   Change the first letter.
            Make something we drink.   _____

PREPOSITIONS

DIRECTIONS: Circle the right answer.

Example: The cat is ___in___ the box.

on
(in)
under

     1. The glove is _____ the table.
on
in
under

2. The table is _____ the chair.
behind
in front of
beside

   3. The dog is _____ the chair.
under
above
in

4. The hat is _____ the bed.
beside
on top of
in

   5. The flowers are _____ the house.
behind
above
in front of

6. The fish is _____ the lake.
in
on
below

   7. The plane is _____ the clouds.
next to
above
below

8. The ribbon is _____ the package.
in
next to
around

   9. The saucer is _____ the cup.
beneath
above
in front of

Name _____ Date _____ Master 4

LET'S COMPARE

DIRECTIONS: Fill in the blank with the correct word.

Example: _____John_____ is shorter than _____Dick_____ .

1. _____'s hair is longer than _____'s hair.

2. _____ is younger than _____ .

3. _____ is wider than _____ .

4. _____ is thinner than _____ .

5. _____ is stronger than _____ .

6. _____ is newer

than _____ .

7. _____ is the heaviest box.

8. _____ is the smallest ball.

9. _____ is the tallest building.

10. _____ is the biggest book.

 John
 Rita
 George
 House A
 Sparky
 Jim

Dick
Carol
Tom
House B
Jocko
Bob

 Mary's car   Ken's car

 A   B   C (50 lbs., 2000 lbs., 500 lbs.)

 A   B   C

  A   B   C

 A   B   C

THE TELEPHONE

DIRECTIONS: Use the chart to find the names of the parts of the telephone. A side number and a top number together show you the letter. (For example, 14=D.) Then find the part on the drawing at the bottom.

	1	2	3	4	5
1	A	B	C	D	E
2	F	G	H	I	J
3	K	L	M	N	O
4	P	Q	R	S	T
5	U	V	W	X	Y/Z

1. 14   24   11   32

2. 43   15   13   15   24   52   15   43

3. 13   35   43   14

4. 13   35   24   34   44   32   35   45

5. 13   35   24   34   43   15   45   51   43   34

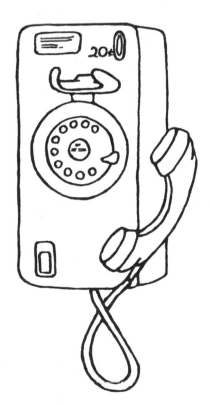

1. _____

2. _____

3. _____

4. _____

5. _____

VERB FIT-IN

DIRECTIONS: Put the correct verb in the boxes on the right.

Example: I _____ my homework last night.
                    (do)

D	I	D

1. I _____ my books from first grade.
         (keep)

2. The telephone _____ a lot last night.
                       (ring)

3. The boy _____ his gloves yesterday.
                  (lose)

4. We _____ for three hours in church last Sunday.
            (sit)

5. I _____ her last year.
          (meet)

6. She _____ me a package last week.
              (send)

7. The Warriors _____ the basketball game.
                      (win)

8. They _____ their house for a lot of money.
              (sell)

9. He _____ his new sweater yesterday.
            (wear)

10. George _____ fast last night.
                  (drive)

11. We _____ breakfast late this morning.
            (eat)

12. I _____ her name yesterday afternoon.
         (forget)

13. Susan _____ a new car last year.
                 (buy)

14. He _____ one hundred miles last summer.
           (swim)

OPPOSITES

DIRECTIONS: Below are incomplete words. Add letters from the bottom. Make words that are opposites.
(Note: Some letters are used more than one time.)

Example: _b_ lack   _w_ hite

1. ___ in   ___ ose   9. ___ ry   ___ et

2. ___ ive   ___ ake   10. ___ bove   ___ elow

3. ___ uy   ___ ell   11. ___ ark   ___ ight

4. ___ ork   ___ lay   12. ___ old   ___ ot

5. ___ it   ___ tand   13. ___ retty   ___ gly

6. ___ sk   ___ nswer   14. ___ ew   ___ ld

7. ___ ight   ___ eft   15. ___ oft   ___ ard

8. ___ sleep   ___ wake

a b c d g h l n o p r s t u w

TIME

DIRECTIONS: Answer the following questions. Use the clocks to help you.

Example: How long did the baby sleep?

three hours

1 How long did George study?

2. How long did Grace practice the piano?

3. How many hours did the class last?

4. How many hours was the TV program on?

5. How many minutes did the cake bake?

6. How many minutes does Ellen have for lunch?

7. How long does Joe work every day?

8. How long do they spend in school every day?

midnight   am

pm   pm

pm   pm

am   am

noon   pm

pm   pm

pm   pm

am   pm

am   pm

BUILD A WORD

DIRECTIONS: Make new words. Add the letter(s) to the word for the picture.

Example: w +   _____hat_____ = _____what_____

1. p +  _____ = _____

2. h +   _____ = _____

3. st +   _____ = _____

4. s +  _____ = _____

5. s +  _____ = _____

6. d +  _____ = _____

7. s +   _____ = _____

8. f +   _____ = _____

9. d +  _____ = _____

10. t +   _____ = _____

RELATIONSHIPS

DIRECTIONS: Use the letters in the boxes to complete the words. Cross out the letters that you use. The letters left will spell a word. Write that word at the bottom.

p	re	su	em	la	pa
ch	ti	cu	on	st	au
te	sh	pl	ip	s	

driver   ___ assenger

teacher   ___ udent

doctor   ___ tient

clerk   ___ stomer

coach   ___ ayer

king   ___ bject

actor   ___ dience

landlord   ___ nant

parent   ___ ild

employee   ___ ployee

— — — — — — — — — — — — —

WHERE ARE YOU?

DIRECTIONS: Follow the directions. Use the map below.

Go to the start.

Drive north.

Turn west on Maple Street.

Go two blocks.

Turn right.

Drive three blocks.

Turn east.

Where are you? _____

WORD STAIRS

DIRECTIONS: Use the words at the bottom to make stairsteps. How many can you make?

Example: T   O   P
                    I
            N   O   W

A C R O S S

ACROSS   HELP   NEXT   TALL

DOWN   KNEE   ROUND   WEEK

ERASER   LUNCH   STUDY   YELLOW

ANIMALS

DIRECTIONS: Unscramble the letters to make the name of an animal. The pictures will help you.

Example: A   C   T      _____ cat

1.   N   A   T   _____

2.   G   O   R   F   _____

3.   P   A   T   H   E   L   E   N    _____

4.   S   O   R   E   H   _____

5.   B   A   R   I   B   T   _____

6.   B   A   R   E   Z   _____

7.   L   O   W   _____

8.   R   E   E   D   _____

9.   W   O   C   _____

10.   D   R   I   B   _____

11.   N   E   C   K   I   C   H   _____

12.   F   L   U   T   Y   B   E   R   T   _____

2 + 2

DIRECTIONS: Draw a line from the words at the left to the correct symbol at the right.

one and nine-tenths	2/7
one-half	.68
multiply	—
equal	%
add	=
one-third	÷
sixty-eight hundredths	1/3
divide	.004
fiftieth	+
percent	0
subtract	×
two-sevenths	1.9
zero	50th
two-fourths	2/4
four-thousandths	1/2

MONEY

DIRECTIONS: Write the names of the coins and bills in the blanks. Then write the correct letters in the numbered blanks at the bottom of the page.

1¢ $\overline{1}\ \overline{2}\ \overline{3}\ \overline{4}\ \overline{5}$

5¢ $\overline{6}\ \overline{7}\ \overline{8}\ \overline{9}\ \overline{10}\ \overline{11}$

10¢ $\overline{12}\ \overline{13}\ \overline{14}\ \overline{15}$

25¢ $\overline{16}\ \overline{17}\ \overline{18}\ \overline{19}\ \overline{20}\ \overline{21}\ \overline{22}$

50¢ $\overline{23}\ \overline{24}\ \overline{25}\ \overline{26}$ $\overline{27}\ \overline{28}\ \overline{29}\ \overline{30}\ \overline{31}\ \overline{32}$

$1 $\overline{33}\ \overline{34}\ \overline{35}$ $\overline{36}\ \overline{37}\ \overline{38}\ \overline{39}\ \overline{40}\ \overline{41}$ $\overline{42}\ \overline{43}\ \overline{44}\ \overline{45}$

$5 $\overline{46}\ \overline{47}\ \overline{48}\ \overline{49}$ $\overline{50}\ \overline{51}\ \overline{52}\ \overline{53}\ \overline{54}\ \overline{55}$ $\overline{56}\ \overline{57}\ \overline{58}\ \overline{59}$

$10 $\overline{60}\ \overline{61}\ \overline{62}$ $\overline{63}\ \overline{64}\ \overline{65}\ \overline{66}\ \overline{67}\ \overline{68}$ $\overline{69}\ \overline{70}\ \overline{71}\ \overline{72}$

$20 $\overline{73}\ \overline{74}\ \overline{75}\ \overline{76}\ \overline{77}\ \overline{78}$ $\overline{79}\ \overline{80}\ \overline{81}\ \overline{82}\ \overline{83}\ \overline{84}$ $\overline{85}\ \overline{86}\ \overline{87}\ \overline{88}$

$50 $\overline{89}\ \overline{90}\ \overline{91}\ \overline{92}\ \overline{93}$ $\overline{94}\ \overline{95}\ \overline{96}\ \overline{97}\ \overline{98}\ \overline{99}$ $\overline{100}\ \overline{101}\ \overline{102}\ \overline{103}$

$\overline{18}$ $\overline{1}\ \overline{10}\ \overline{34}\ \overline{62}\ \overline{78}$ $\overline{24}\ \overline{48}\ \overline{15}\ \overline{94}$ $\overline{70}$ $\overline{31}$ $\overline{1}\ \overline{75}\ \overline{3}\ \overline{4}\ \overline{93}$

$\overline{61}\ \overline{67}\ \overline{99}\ \overline{76}\ \overline{35}\ \overline{50}$

© National Textbook Company

THE BUS STATION

DIRECTIONS: Put the cities in alphabetical order. Then write the correct letters in the numbered blanks at the bottom of the page.

You want to buy a bus ticket. Buses go to the following cities:

SAN ANTONIO	NEW YORK	DENVER
NEW ORLEANS	PITTSBURGH	LAS VEGAS
DALLAS	MIAMI	SAN FRANCISCO
PORTLAND	ATLANTA	BOSTON

1. __ __ $\underline{7}$ __ $\underline{14}$ __ __

2. __ __ __ __ __ __
   $\underline{4}$

3. __ __ __ __ __ $\underline{6}$

4. __ $\underline{18}$ __ $\underline{10}$ __ __

5. __ __ __   __ $\underline{3}$ __ __ __

6. $\underline{17}$ __ $\underline{9}$ __ __

7. __ __ __   __ __ __ __ __ __
   $\underline{8}$

8. __ __ __   __ __ __ __
   $\underline{11}$

9. __ __ __ __ __ __ $\underline{5}$ __ __ $\underline{2}$

10. __ $\underline{13}$ __ $\underline{15}$ __ __ __ __

11. __ __ __   __ __ $\underline{1}$ __ __ __

12. __ __ __   __ __ __ __ $\underline{16}$ __ __
    $\underline{12}$

$\overline{1}$ $\overline{2}$ $\overline{3}$ $\overline{4}$ $\overline{5}$ $\overline{6}$ $\overline{7}$ $\overline{8}$ $\overline{9}$ $\overline{10}$ $\overline{11}$ $\overline{12}$ $\overline{13}$ $\overline{14}$ $\overline{15}$ $\overline{16}$ $\overline{17}$ $\overline{18}$!

CARS

DIRECTIONS: Fill in the blanks with the correct words from the bottom of the page.

headlight	door	tire
roof	trunk	windshield
bumper	tail light	steering wheel
door handle	gas tank	hood

TWO-WORD VERBS

DIRECTIONS: Complete the sentences using the words below. (Note: Some words are used more than once.) Then fill in the numbered blanks at the bottom.

through   on   out   up   off   back   down   over   in

1. Cassy blew __ __ the balloon.

2. We sent __ __ __ __ the package.
   <u>1</u>

3. They tore __ __ __ __ the old building.

4. Jennifer likes to look __ __ __ __ __ __ __ catalogs.
   <u>3</u>

5. Walter blew __ __ __ the candles on his cake.
   <u>7</u>

6. Please stand __ __ straight.

7. They took __ __ __ __ their Christmas presents.
   <u>6</u>

8. Would you like to try __ __ the shoes?

9. He said to the gas station owner, "Fill 'er __ __ ."

10. Look __ __ the word in the dictionary.

11. Tear __ __ __ the top part of the page.

12. Bruce likes to try __ __ __ a car before he buys it.
    <u>2</u>

13. The Smiths came __ __ __ __ for dinner last night.
    <u>5</u> <u>4</u>

14. The clerk took __ __ __ __ the information.

15. Hand __ __ your homework tomorrow.   __ __ __ __ __ __ __!
                                                1 2 3 4 5 6 7

AT THE RESTAURANT

DIRECTIONS: Use the words at the bottom to fill in the crossword puzzle.

ACROSS

1. money given to the waiter

2. This coffee is _____ !

4. a drink

6. a kind of beef

11. list of food

12. person who makes the food

13. _____ and pepper

DOWN

2. short name for Coca-Cola™

3. ice cream, apple pie, etc.

4. person who takes the money

5. main dish

6. lettuce and tomato _____

7. a drink

8. person who takes your order

10. mid-day meal

cashier	dessert	salt
coffee	entree	steak
Coke	lunch	tea
cold	menu	tip
cook	salad	waiter

SIGNS

DIRECTIONS: Draw a line between the sign and the place where you would find it.

R𝗑	movie theater
Lead-free $1.27/gal.	restaurant
ALL FLIGHTS ON TIME	drug store
FOR RENT	apartment
Next feature: 10 P.M.	airport
QUIET PLEASE!	park
SPEED LIMIT 55 MPH	gas station
U.S. MAIL	highway

parking lot

supermarket

bus

shoe store

taxi

post office

library

eggs 79¢/dozen
DON'T PICK THE FLOWERS
LOT FILLED
We have YOUR size!
NOT FOR HIRE
Exact Change only
OPEN FOR BREAKFAST *TRY OUR COFFEE*

ADJECTIVES

DIRECTIONS: Count the syllables in the underlined adjectives. Put the words into the right list at the bottom of the page.

Example: This is an <u>easy</u> book.   **Two syllables**

1. I live on the <u>fifth</u> floor.

2. He found the <u>secret</u> message.

3. My professor is very <u>intelligent</u>.

4. Today three students are <u>absent</u>.

5. There are twelve <u>underlined</u> words.

6. Students are always <u>busy</u>.

7. She sent a <u>registered</u> letter.

8. My grandfather is an <u>educated</u> man.

9. This shirt is <u>cheap</u>.

10. The letter was very <u>personal</u>.

11. These answers are <u>correct</u>.

12. The line is <u>horizontal</u>.

One Syllable	Two Syllables	Three Syllables	Four Syllables
1. _____	1. _____	1. _____	1. _____
2. _____	2. _____	2. _____	2. _____
	3. _____	3. _____	3. _____
	4. _____		

PAIRS

DIRECTIONS: Write a word in the blanks that makes a pair with the underlined word. Then fill in the numbered blanks at the bottom.

Example: I'll have <u>bacon</u> and e g g s .

1. Please pass the <u>salt</u> and __ __ __ __ __ __ .
                              1

2. I have been <u>up</u> and __ __ __ __ the stairs a hundred times.
                         2   3

3. She doesn't know <u>right</u> from __ __ __ __ __ .
                                        4

4. The children were <u>in</u> and __ __ __ of the house all day.

5. He doesn't know his <u>left</u> hand from his __ __ __ __ __ .
                                                    5

6. They fought like <u>cats</u> and __ __ __ __ .
                                   6

7. They look like <u>brother</u> and __ __ __ __ __ __ __ .

8. The car cost an <u>arm</u> and a __ __ __ .

9. He walked <u>back</u> and __ __ __ __ __ all night.
                            7

10. Mr. and Mrs. Kent are just like my <u>aunt</u> and __ __ __ __ __ .
                                                          8

11. That's the <u>long</u> and the __ __ __ __ __ of it.

12. He wants a new <u>ball</u> and __ __ __ .
                                  9

13. I dropped my <u>knife</u> and __ __ __ __ .

14. They are as different as <u>night</u> and __ __ __ .
                                              10 11 12

15. It's an <u>open</u> and __ __ __ __ case.

__ __ __ __   __ __ __   __ __ __ __ __ !
7 5 3 1   9 4 2   6 11 8 10 12

ADVERBS

DIRECTIONS: Make ten sentences using phrases from groups A, B, and C.

Example: We worked slowly.

A	**B**	**C**
It	are going to arrive	late.
He	ate soup	quickly.
The teachers	rode the bicycles	easily.
I	like to read	slowly.
They	walked to the store	fast.
She	spoke French	quietly.
We	worked	loudly.
You	will play the piano	well.
The students	talk to everyone	badly.
You and I	are going to finish	early.

1. _____

2. _____

3. _____

4. _____

5. _____

6. _____

7. _____

8. _____

9. _____

10. _____

SCHEDULES

DIRECTIONS: Circle the letter of the correct choice. Then write the letters at the bottom.

First semester	
8:00	history
9:00	English
10:00	math

This is a _____ schedule.

    Q. library
    R. class
    S. museum

Today's Flights	
1 pm	Buffalo
2 pm	Toronto
3 pm	New York

This is a(n) _____ schedule.

    I. airline
    J. bus
    K. train

The Vikings	
Sat. March 10	Warriors
Sat. March 17	Hawks
Sat. March 24	Bears

This is a _____ schedule.

    E. zoo
    F. bus
    G. sports

Tuesday	
9 am	breakfast with Joe
10 am	meeting with Mr. Smith
noon	lunch with company president

This is a(n) _____ schedule.

    H. appointment
    I. class
    J. sports

The Blue Zephyr	
Lv.	8:32 am
Ar.	9:07 am — Fort Smith
Ar.	11:30 am — Little Rock

This is a(n) _____ schedule.

    T. train
    U. appointment
    V. doctor's

_ _ _ _ _!

CROSSWORD VERBS

DIRECTIONS: Write the correct verb in the puzzle.

Example: Susie _____ pizza.
                      (like)

L I K E S

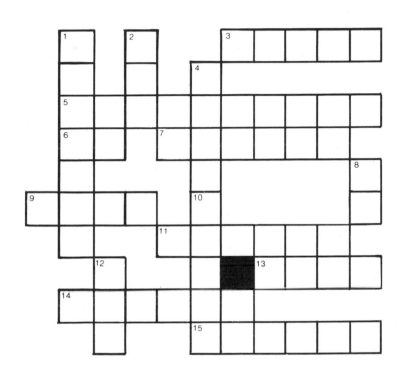

ACROSS

3. Don't _____ late tomorrow.
   (sleep)

5. We _____ the play last night.
   (understand)

6. Jesse forgot to _____ his homework.
   (do)

7. Tom _____ his car every Saturday.
   (wash)

9. Six students _____ sick yesterday.
   (be)

11. I _____ to the store tomorrow.
    (go)

13. John _____ the meeting early this morning.
    (leave)

14. They _____ home from school yesterday.
    (walk)

15. Rose _____ Spanish very well.
    (speak)

DOWN

1. Henry _____ German last year.
   (study)

2. Please _____ these numbers.
   (add)

4. Ann _____ piano every day.
   (practice)

8. Don't _____ late for class tomorrow.
   (be)

12. She _____ ten years old last week.
    (be)

BACKWARD/FORWARD WORDS

DIRECTIONS: Some words are written the same backward and forward. Draw a line from the definition at the left to the correct word on the right.

1. twelve o'clock in the day	mom
2. something you drink	did
3. another word for <u>mother</u>	Bob
4. a tiny child	SOS
5. past tense of <u>do</u>	bib
6. something a baby wears	pep
7. another name for <u>Robert</u>	sis
8. a call for help	noon
9. an exclamation	Wow!
10. energy	tot
11. short for <u>sister</u>	dad
12. another word for <u>father</u>	pop

THE MOVIES

DIRECTIONS: Unscramble the sentences. Rewrite them on the lines at the bottom of the page.

Example: like / do you / movies   Do you like movies?

1. to the movies / to go / everyone likes

2. different kinds / of movies / people prefer

3. Westerns / likes / my father

4. mysteries / my mother / likes

5. prefers / my brother / science fiction

6. my sister / love stories / chooses

7. always wants / monster movies / my best friend / to see

8. go / my other friends / to comedies

9. to everything / go / I

10. the popcorn / love / I

1. _____

2. _____

3. _____

4. _____

5. _____

6. _____

7. _____

8. _____

9. _____

10. _____

TELEVISION

DIRECTIONS: Find the following words in the puzzle. Circle them.

antenna	games	sports
black and white	movies	television
cartoons	news	TV set
channel	program	UHF
color	soap opera	weather

A	T	B	T	V	S	E	T	C	D	E	F	G
H	E	C	I	J	O	K	L	M	N	O	P	W
B	L	A	C	K	A	N	D	W	H	I	T	E
G	E	R	N	Q	P	R	O	G	R	A	M	A
A	V	T	E	M	O	V	I	E	S	R	R	T
M	I	O	W	S	P	O	R	T	S	T	U	H
E	S	O	S	V	E	W	X	Y	Z	A	B	E
S	I	N	D	E	R	F	G	C	O	L	O	R
H	O	S	C	H	A	N	N	E	L	I	J	K
A	N	T	E	N	N	A	L	M	U	H	F	N

FAST FOOD AND SNACKS

DIRECTIONS: Unscramble the letters to make a word. Write the word in the blank.

Example: A ___snack___ is something eaten between meals.
                        kasnc

Americans are always in a hurry. Sometimes for breakfast they eat

_____ and _____ or instant _____ .
      studno   feefoc   acerel

At lunch they sometimes have _____ or _____
                                        oth sodg   srebmarug h

and _____ . Instant _____ is eaten too.
      chenfr risef   opsu

Sometimes for dinner they order _____ or _____ .
                                          pizaz   ridef neckich

Other times they cook a _____ .
                              VT nidren

Americans like to have snacks, too. At movies they buy _____ ,
                                                              ydanc

_____ , and _____ . Watching television, they sometimes have
      norpcop   tofs nirdsk

_____ or _____ .
      atpoto spich   zepsletr

THE POST OFFICE

DIRECTIONS: Match the first part of each sentence with the second part. Draw a line between them. Then rewrite the sentences at the bottom of the page.

1. I went to the post office		very long.
2. I also wanted to buy.		the package first class.
3. The line was		home slowly.
4. But it moved		was closed.
5. I sent		to mail a package.
6. The cost was		something.
7. I walked		buy the stamps.
8. Then I remembered		very quickly.
9. I forgot to		$2.40.
10. When I returned, the post office		some stamps.

1. _____

2. _____

3. _____

4. _____

5. _____

6. _____

7. _____

8. _____

9. _____

10. _____

MUSIC! MUSIC! MUSIC!

DIRECTIONS: Make new words from the words below.

Example: **SONG**

no
go
so

RADIO

_____

_____

_____

_____

_____

STEREO

_____

_____

_____

_____

_____

RECORD

_____

_____

_____

_____

_____

SPEAKERS

_____

_____

_____

_____

_____

_____

_____

CASSETTE TAPE

_____

_____

_____

_____

_____

_____

_____

HEADPHONES

_____

_____

_____

_____

_____

_____

_____

AT THE BANK

DIRECTIONS: Put the following sentences in order to make a story. Then write the story in the blanks which are below the sentences.

He gave me twenties and tens.

I stood in line for fifteen minutes.

She helped me open a savings account.

Yesterday I went to the bank.

The officer gave me a free gift for opening the account.

I asked the teller to cash my check.

Then I went to speak to one of the officers.

I'll go again next week.

1. _____

2. _____

3. _____

4. _____

5. _____

6. _____

7. _____

8. _____